I BUILT A STONE AGE HOUSE

I BUILT A
STONE AGE HOUSE

Hans-Ole Hansen

Translated from the Danish by
Maurice Michael

WITH 31 PHOTOGRAPHS AND
11 LINE DRAWINGS

THE JOHN DAY COMPANY   NEW YORK

Contents

Illustrations

DRAWINGS IN TEXT

1. The Riddle of the Past

A LONG, long time ago, in the days known as the Stone Age, much of the world was not only unknown but also uninhabited. In northern Europe, where I live, it was only along the rivers and the seacoasts that people lived, and they were hunters and fishermen who did not even till the soil. Then, out of the East, came new peoples with greater skills and herds of domestic cattle. They knew how to till the soil and grow crops. These peoples had many names, and among them was one tribe or people called Danes, who finally settled in what is now known as Denmark.

Such people, of course, could neither read nor write and we have no record of their doings, which we know only from the evidence of the things they abandoned or threw away which we have found in bogs and the sites of their houses, or in their graves. Skill these people certainly had, for they were able to build with enormous blocks of stone (megaliths), piling one on top of the other to make what we suppose were graves (cromlechs or dolmens), in which they buried their chiefs and princes. As with the great stones of Easter Island, people used to refuse to believe that these could have been built by primitive people and so the credit for these feats was given to "giants" or supernatural beings. The early chroniclers of our history knew no better, and they wrote that our country must at one time have been inhabited by a race of giants, strong enough to build with such enormous stones. When you see them perched, like that in the illustration on page 12, on the top of a hill, you too can find it difficult to believe that primitive people, living a thousand years ago and more, without engineering skill or suitable tools, could have got such stones to their sites, let alone piled one on top of the other.

Thanks to the work of the archaeologists, we now know quite a lot about these early inhabitants of our country, who were neither supernatural beings nor giants; in fact, they were small of stature, but obviously clever with their hands and possessed of more skills than one could expect of those who lived so long ago.

11

I. Huge and silent, the megalithic tomb broods over its secret. Can we wrest the secret from it?

The further back in time you go, the more difficult it is to learn about the people who lived then: what they wore, ate, did and looked like. To find this out is the job of the archaeologist, who is a sort of detective, hunting for clues and fitting together pieces of an infinity of puzzles to provide facts or likely suppositions. I have always thought this a thrilling and fascinating job and, as a boy, I wanted to be an archaeologist. I wanted to do it on my own, but excavation is a lengthy and expensive business and it is seldom that the amateur lone wolf is able to indulge it, if he has such a secret passion. Really, one ought never to work alone, for every little thing of interest has to be measured and numbered and treated so that it can be preserved in a museum. In each "dig"

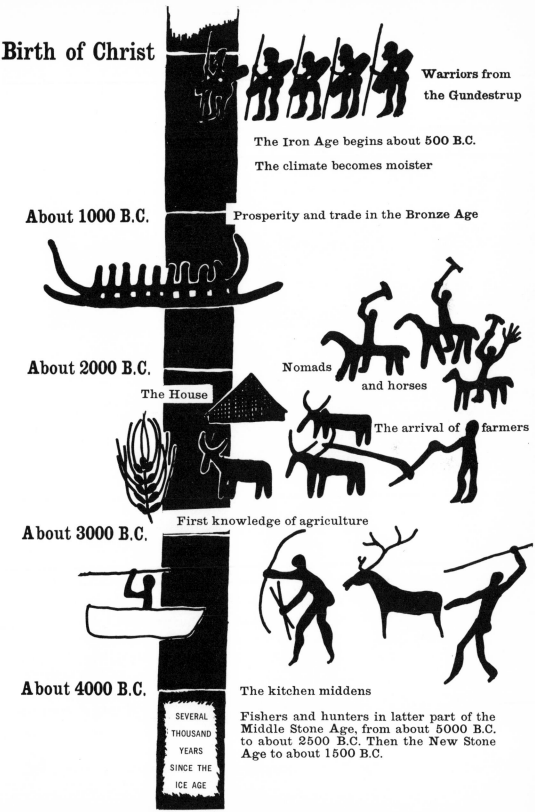

Birth of Christ

Warriors from
the Gundestrup

The Iron Age begins about 500 B.C.
The climate becomes moister

About 1000 B.C.   Prosperity and trade in the Bronze Age

About 2000 B.C.

Nomads
and horses

The House

The arrival of farmers

First knowledge of agriculture

About 3000 B.C.

About 4000 B.C.   The kitchen middens

SEVERAL
THOUSAND
YEARS
SINCE THE
ICE AGE

Fishers and hunters in latter part of the
Middle Stone Age, from about 5000 B.C.
to about 2500 B.C. Then the New Stone
Age to about 1500 B.C.

1. This shows the succession of ages in Denmark. The Gundestrup is the site of
important Bronze Age finds.

there can be ten thousand, in fact a hundred thousand different objects, ranging from mouse-nibbled nutshells to boats made of hollowed tree trunks. Even the tiniest microscopic part of a plant can reveal something about the seasons, people's way of life, and the plants that grew there then, and today we can discover much more about an excavated dwelling place than was possible a mere twenty years ago. That is one of the reasons why it is bad for the inexperienced to excavate mounds and ancient dwelling places. Take yourself: would you not be more interested in a polished stone ax than in some greasy bits of charcoal or some crumbling human bones? Yet if you overlooked the latter you would miss—and perhaps destroy—a lot.

There is so much in the big museums that if you try to see everything at once you just become tired and bewildered, so it is much more sensible just to have a thorough look at the things in one or two rooms and leave the rest for another day. When you take time and can inspect things closely, you will find that they have a life and individuality of their own.

There, for example, is the big storage jar some mother used in her kitchen and home. Here and there on it is the impress of a grain of wheat or barley, showing you what used to grow in the fields where the jar came from. You can almost feel the light summer breeze blowing across those tiny yellow fields and see the ripe grain billowing. Beside it is father's stone ax, with which he used to fell trees and knock a cow on the head when he had to slaughter one. What was he doing when it broke, snapping off at the haft like that? In the National Museum in Denmark you can see something rather grim and uncanny: the head of a Stone Age man who had been killed by two long arrows. How and why? Once you start asking such questions you quickly find yourself immersed in the history of a particular place, from the day it was founded until it burned down a couple of generations later.

When I was your age, however, I did not think that looking at things in glass cases was enough; it left me feeling that something was lacking. I wanted to be able to handle the things and use them, but there was a stupid pane of glass between them and me. Then I had an idea: I could copy all these things and have them at home in my own room, and use them when and as often as I liked. It would be like living in the Stone Age. And if I were going to copy Stone Age things, I should come up against all the difficulties and so, perhaps, discover some of the finer points of craftsmanship that the Stone Age man and his wife had been familiar with, but of which no record or knowledge remains. And so I began, but unfortunately at first I muffed everything I tried to make; my earthenware pots collapsed and my bits of bone snapped—so I gave up the idea. But I could not stop reading about the things and imagining what the lives of my forefathers must have been like in pre-historic times.

Then I began digging on my own. At first I wasn't very successful in this either, because I was digging where I ought not to have dug and so always had to be on my guard and keep on the lookout in order to avoid discovery. You can't do much in such circumstances, and I realize now that it was all pretty silly.

But then, one wet, cold afternoon, far out on the moor I discovered a number of stones that a plow had turned up, and among them a jumble of bits of charcoal, even big pieces of charred wood. I could see that these were the remains of a house, and when I found a stone ax among the charcoal I realized it must be a Stone Age house. The ax was ground and smooth, which meant that it was from the New Stone Age, that is, dating from about 2500 b.c. to 1500 b.c.

I stayed there until it was too dark to distinguish any further details, stood there wet and muddy, trying to imagine how the house must have looked and who the people were who had lived in it and what they were like. This attempt at mental reconstruction made me suddenly feel that I wanted to build it up again. I could see it with gleaming yellow straw roof and walls. When I had built it, I told myself, I would fill it with all the things I could make myself, but of course only things that belonged to its period.

I could not get the crazy idea out of my head, and all that evening I talked of nothing but the Stone Age house I was going to build. Such things, of course, are easier said than done. I know that now, though I did not realize it at the time. What I wanted to try was, to use a rather high-sounding technical expression, an experiment in reconstruction.

Can you imagine the jumble of things lying there at my feet in the twilight, well plastered with sticky peat soil? Somewhere underneath, perhaps, there would be post marks, dark patches in the lighter subsoil where the posts of the house had stood. But, of course, it wasn't even certain that such posts would have belonged to the house I had found.

And it was on the foundations of such vague traces that I wanted to try to build a house, a whole big house!

Everything that had been above ground had to be invented. Not that "invented" is the right word. I couldn't just build the house as I imagined it must have been. I had to learn about old farmsteads and read books

15

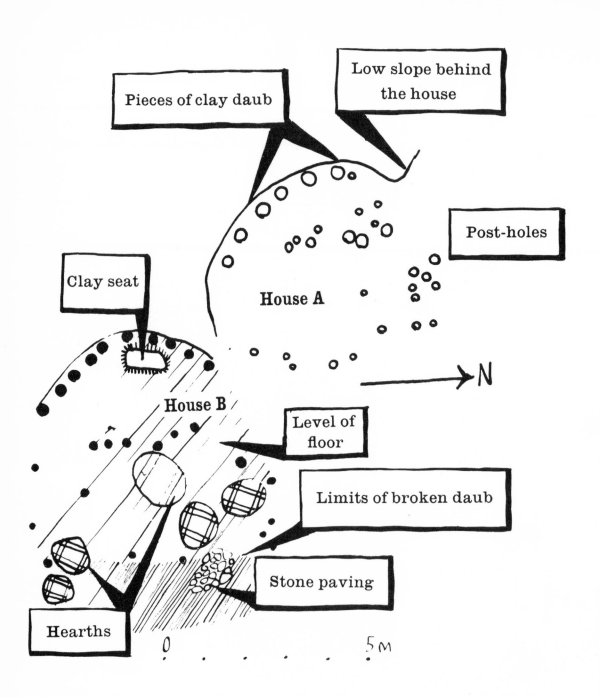

Pieces of clay daub

Low slope behind the house

Post-holes

Clay seat

House A

House B

Level of floor

Limits of broken daub

Stone paving

Hearths

N

0   5 M

2. Site XXXII at Troldebjerg, excavated by Jens Winther and described by him in his paper *Troldebjerg 1–2* (published in Rudkøbing, 1935–6). I based my model on House B.

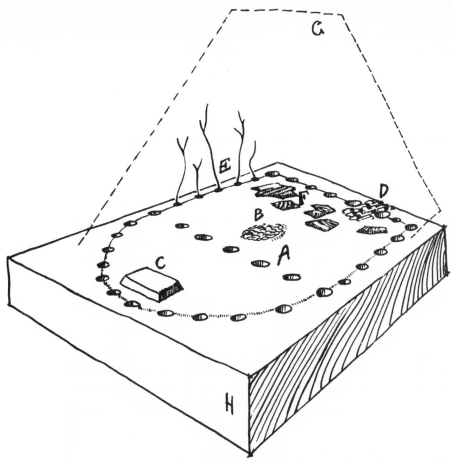

3. I made a model showing what the archaeologist found when he excavated the site of House B (Fig. 2).

A, Post holes. A line has been drawn between these post holes following the outer wall. This shows the limit of the layer of trodden earth, charcoal from the hearth, and pieces of broken earthen vessels that belonged to the interior.   B, The hearth. Stones made brittle by fire.   C, Earthen bench.   D, Entrance paving. On either side is a post hole for the two doorposts.   E, Willow twigs that I stuck into the ground to show where our holes should be dug.   F, Remains of the burned wattle-and-daub wall were found here and these showed that the gable had been a mud wall. On these pieces I have drawn the impress of branches, for it was those that told us that the inside of the wall was a wattle skeleton.   G, Outline of the finished house.   H, The wooden base on which the model house was built, representing the ground.

on archaeology to discover what they had to say about primitive houses in all sorts of places, and about the prehistoric finds made in neighboring countries. Then I had to make lengthy calculations and build models. When I was bored in school, I used to draw roof gradients and make sketches of how the house might look.

17

Gradually some of my ideas began to take shape and have some justification. In the end I decided on one plan that seemed most likely to be correct. Obviously there were still plenty of mistakes in it. Some, I hoped, would be corrected when we began to build the actual full-sized house, unless I was so far out in my calculations that the whole thing collapsed!

If a Stone Age man could have come to life again and seen the models I made, I expect he would have flung himself down and laughed until he cried. That is why I called it an *experiment* in reconstruction. No one was going to catch me saying that I intended to build a Stone Age house as it really had been, but only as it might have been.

Now here is the problem with which I was faced. Try it for yourself before I go on to tell the story of what happened and how we fared.

Figure 2 is an archaeologist's plan of the site on which I based my experiment, and includes information given in his report on his excavations. See if you can reckon from this how the house must have looked or *could* have looked, which is what I had to do. Figure 3 shows the way I made a model of House B at the site. If you think your ideas are better than mine, all right, or if you feel that mine are better than yours, I won't quarrel with that either. It will just show how difficult it is to arrive at the truth, or how many possible ways there are of interpreting facts.

2. The Stone Ax with the Black Haft

FROM THE start of my experiment I was determined to be consistent. That meant that I was to make my own Stone Age tools (and use no others) and employ only the materials and techniques of the Stone Age. (Though later, as you will see, I had to compromise for the sake of speed.)

The first thing I needed seemed to be an ax. Here I was exceptionally lucky. There were plenty of Stone Age axheads to be had, and I felt that I could well afford to sacrifice one or two, if need be, on my experiment. Hafts, however, are rare indeed. Wind, weather, and the years in their thousands have crumbled them all away. It is fearfully rare for a haft to be found intact and for it to be possible to preserve it. There was, however, one such treasure in a special showcase in the National Museum. I was given its measurements and a cardboard pattern of its shape, and so I set to work. At the same time I read up the details of the haft found in a bog at Stevns in Zealand years before, and which archaeologists had tried to copy in oak.

The handles of garden tools and the hafts of hammers are made of ash, which is far and away the toughest wood for this purpose, and I decided to make my haft of ash too. So I went to our joiner and used some of my meager savings to buy a piece of seasoned ash thick enough to take the hole for the stone axhead, that is over four inches thick. Mine was to be a haft that would last, so I took a lot of trouble about shaping it. I didn't saw it, both because they had no saws in the Stone Age and because, if I had, the surface would not have followed the grain of the wood as it should.

In Switzerland there is a wonderful collection of Stone Age wooden objects, because there the people of the Stone Age lived in villages built on piles out into lakes, so that everything they threw away fell into the water, which gave it a better chance of being preserved. There I saw a Stone Age ax haft that had not even been finished, so that I could distinctly see how it had been chopped and shaped with another stone ax. I should have liked to use a stone ax to shape my haft, but I soon saw that, being quite unfamiliar with the technique, it would take me far too long were I to do so, so I compromised and used a steel ax in order to get the haft finished quickly. (I discovered later that it is a small, light stone ax you should use for this sort of joiner's job.)

When I had shaped my haft I began making the holes for the ax head. This I did properly, boring my hole as the Stone Age people did, using a piece of stick and coarse sand. It isn't an easy job boring through anything as thick as that haft's head of seasoned ash, but it can be done provided you have plenty of time. In this respect the hafts of Stone Age axes must have been as costly as the heads.

My finishing touch was to put the haft into our furnace and keep it there while I counted ten. Then I pulled it out and quickly scraped off what was charred and glowing. It had a smell like new bread. That treatment made the surface of the wood smooth and almost impervious to damp. (The dwelling places of the Stone Age were mostly by the shores of lakes or bank bogs, so they must have been very damp.) There my haft was; smooth and glistening like ebony or bog oak.

Then came the exciting moment when I put the axhead into the hole and went out to try out my ax. It was my first real tool.

I stole out into the garden. There weren't so many trees worth felling and those that were, of course, I wasn't meant to touch. I selected one as far as possible from windows and listening ears, right in the middle of the hedge that acted as windbreak for the house. It was a good-sized tree with a short trunk, but in such a position that if I could just make it fall the right way and drag it clear and away, there would be no visible gap and no one would notice that there was a tree missing.

I took a good grip and set to work, chopping so that chips flew in all directions. I had to stop every now and again to straighten my back, but it was amazing what progress I made. I inspected the edge of my ax: not a chip in it. Not yet at any rate. As long as I chopped in a definite way, that is with short quick chops, all went splendidly, and after about twenty minutes a dull creak and a groan told me that I had done it. I went and stood aside out of the way and, for the first time, had a proper view of the gaping wound in the trunk. It looked as though beavers had been gnawing at it, and I saw to my horror that the wound was directly in line with the lawn and the house!

Then the tree went. It crashed through our hedge and landed with a dull roar right across the lawn. What a long tree it was. My face was burning. I had felled one of our poplars! One of our landmarks! Then I heard the garden door open and the sound of quick, brisk footsteps. Should I say that it was the work of the wind? That a sudden gust had blown it over?

3. The Great Sun God and the Chicken

WHAT WITH the gnawed end of the trunk and other things, my suggestion of the poplar's fall being the work of a sudden gust of wind was not accepted. Since then I have made many stone-ax hafts and felled lots of trees, but I haven't touched any more of our poplars, tulip trees, chestnuts, copper beeches, or other exotic sorts that we have; I have confined my attentions to wild ashes and elms, which are the trees that provided the wood used in making the first trial house.

Having no one to whom I could go and say: "Excuse me, but do you know how much clay you need for thirty-six square yards of wattle, and how many withes will it take to make that amount of wattle?" I just had to try to work it out for myself.

Another question was: where to build the house? In our garden? That would be a waste of good soil, I was told. But what about the field behind our garden, a whole corner of which had been filled with stones that generation after generation of farmers had collected off the other, bigger fields? For years that corner with its heaps of stones had been our playground; we had made roads and bridges, built castles and ramparts there. With its sun-warmed stones and dense forests of nettles, the place was almost symbolic of prehistoric days. It was just the sort of place where the first farmers could have settled and laboriously cleaned one little patch of ground after the other for their fields, built themselves a house, and gradually produced farmland out of the wilderness. The highest point would have been the site for their colorful burial chamber, the barrow that gave them good fortune and protection. I decided that that was the site for the house.

My voice shook and stammered as I told the man who owned the land what the idea was and what exactly I wanted to do. He gave me his permission, for, as he said, what I built could always be removed. Anyway, he was an understanding person and not one to make difficulties.

Day after day I went to that corner of the field with the stones, and

21

II. There stood our first daub house glowing in the morning sunlight, and in front of it the grim sacrificial stone.

gradually I cleared a site. Now and again I cut a finger or thumb on a flint, and when that happened I took care to wipe as much blood as I could onto a big stone I had found and earmarked as our sacred stone, a proper sacrificial stone.

For a long time I thought that I should never get the site cleared, but I persevered, telling myself to remember my forefathers and how they had struggled with stones all their lives. They were born among stones, humped stones year in and year out as they cleaned their little fields and built their tombs of great heavy stones. The thought of that helped me to keep going, and then I got a friend to come and lend a hand, and after that the work shot ahead.

Since this was only a trial house, I shall not tell you all about how we built it, but save the details for Chapter 5 and the story of the big house many of my friends helped to build.

One fine day the trial house was ready. It was wedged between great heaps of stones, but we both thought it was magnificent. That night, of course, we had to sleep in it. We lit the first fire to christen the hearth and watched and tended it as anxiously as if the house had been drenched with gasoline.

By the flickering light that fell through the doorway, I painted special primitive signs on the gory sacred stone and then carefully shrouded it with a blanket, because the great Sun God must not shine upon it before a certain moment. That stone with all its colorful power and authority was to protect the house, bring us good fortune for the future, and keep enemies at bay.

The question of what we were to sacrifice called for a lot of consideration. I first thought of one of the little boys who cycled past along the road every day on their way to school, for I knew that on very solemn occasions and in moments of crisis the people of the Stone Age often sacrificed and ate a human being. But the possibility that after such an initiation visitors might be put off and afraid to come and see us, lest they share the same fate, made me abandon the idea. The next suggestion was a cow, but one didn't need all that amount of blood, so in the end we decided on a chicken.

"Of course they didn't have hens in the Stone or Bronze Age," I said, "but in view of the circumstances we must just pretend that it's a cow or an ox we are sacrificing to our dead kin up on the hill and to our two mighty gods, the Sun God and the god of our axes."

And when we had pooled our resources there was only just enough to buy the chicken. "Cheep-cheep," went the chick. It really is a shame and a pity it has to die, I thought. There's no real point in it, is there? And suppose it haunts the place and we are never free of it? "Cheep-cheep," said the chicken again from the darkness outside. A trickle of smoke rose from the embers on the hearth. Aren't you being soft? You don't have the true, tough Stone Age mentality, I thought, and rolled over onto the other side.

Thus I debated the matter. I tried to think of how on earth to kill the chick, then I wondered how it would be if I let it go and didn't bother

III. Then came the day when a new house appeared beside the first. The sacrificial stone had to be moved, so the early morning sunlight could fall on it once more.

about the Sun God, my dead kinsmen in the barrow on top of the hill, the God of the Axes, and the whole horde of evil and friendly beings.

In the end day broke. Feverishly I woke my companion. "It's time now, wake up, we've got to do it." My voice was thick.

There was something lying in the doorway—two axes, hafts crossed.

"Cheep-cheep," went the chicken, and pecked at a blade of grass.

"Have you seen that? During the night some good spirit has come and laid those two axes before our door," I said in amazement.

We studied them.

"There are prints here," said my companion.

"Those are Mother's. She must have tried to surprise us and been halted by the spirits of the stone. That's a good sign indeed for the quality of our work. We won't need to kill the chicken at all, for the sacred stone has already got power enough from *my* blood. If the mighty ones have stood guard over us during the night and even sent us gifts, no more is needed."

Then in a loud voice, so that the mighty one could hear, I said, "The tracks have nothing to do with the axes, which are the gift of friendly beings."

I felt hugely relieved.

"Let the chicken go," I commanded.

"Go in peace, you poor little brute," I muttered, as it stepped out of its basket.

Then we pulled the cover off the sacred stone.

The sunlight shone on the fresh paint and the power of the stone spread all around us, penetrated into all the plants and animals and up into ourselves, promising well for the future of the house.

"Cheep-cheep," said the chicken, and scratched in a patch of loose earth.

When we built a second house, which we called the long house, we had to move the sacred stone, as you can see in Plate III.

4. The Frozen Clay Pit

OUR FIRST farmers were faced with the same problems as the early settlers in America. The Stone Age farmers who came to Denmark found it so trackless and closely forested that it must have appeared hopeless to think of ever making fields there. But the soil was good and the land empty. While farther south there were hostile, warlike tribes everywhere, here was peace. Only along the coast were a few shy, poor hunters and fishermen, people who had long known about wheat and grew tiny patches of it just up from the beach. Where the new arrivals wanted to go was covered with continuous forest. From the air the country would have looked like a stretch of plush, with glints of silver from the various rivers and lakes to show off the dark green. Many of these lakes have since filled up and are now moor or grassland. Then almost the only open stretches of grass were along the watercourses, and to follow them was the only way it was possible to penetrate inland.

Penetrate inland? That sounds as if they had to contend with lianas and tree ferns in a jungle, which, of course, they didn't; but progress must have been slow and laborious all the same, because they had large herds of oxen, as well as flocks of sheep and goats and long-legged pigs which were the most difficult of all to keep together. An agricultural tribe on the move must have been a vast horde of animals and people, and one can imagine the commotion of shouting and lowing, bleating and grunting as slowly it made its way up the grass verges of the river, or laboriously struggled through the forest.

The lowing of the cattle must have been in the ears of these immigrant people all the time. They must have been born with it in their ears, for their journeys took a long time, and babies were born on the march or in the places which they had thought were their journey's end, but then abandoned when they heard of better land farther on.

The native hunters peering from their hiding places must have been amazed at the sight of this strange procession slowly moving past, the sun glinting on long horns and glossy flanks. Never can the hunters have seen so much meat at one time, but for all the seeming confusion there were grim men with long spears guarding the cattle, and the hunters did not dare venture from their hiding places.

To and fro, to and fro swung the earthenware vessels that dangled in the black-haired women's carrying nets.

Then one day the tribe halted in a clearing beside a great bog. The oak forest came down to its very edge, and here and there a giant had fallen into the mire and was lying, its bare, angular branches festooned with yards of trailing lichen that made it look like some great monster. Above the bog hung a veritable umbrella of birds, most of them kinds that we have today—swans, graylag geese, duck, grebe, and ugly cormorants. Their cries could be heard deep within the forest.

The trees in the forest grew close together, and the oaks were tall and slender, quite unlike ours today. The floor of the forest was sour and it was a hard job transforming it into mold that would grow a farmer's crops. In the forest were foxes and lynxes, and the people would catch glimpses of wolves and bears in some distant clearing. The hunters sought red deer and roe deer or snuffling wild pig.

Beavers swarmed in the rivers, where they had their dams and pools. Along the grasslands and bog grew willows and oaks. Birch and hazel were just waiting for opportunities to spread to where the oaks had reigned supreme before these new people appeared, in whose carts hung bags of plantain seed, that faithful companion of those who till the land.

Such, roughly, were the lands that these first tillers of the soil had made their own.

These new arrivals had armed themselves against the wilderness with heavy double-edged axes, and now the silence of the forest was broken by other sounds than the cries of animals and the calls of birds: the first heavy ax strokes. More and more axes could be heard; soon the strokes were ringing out in most purposeful unison. Now and again there would be a loud crash and the echo of it would roll on and on into the forest until it reached the hunters, who understood nothing of all this.

Slowly the smoke began to ascend from the burning piles of twigs and branches, rising into the still, blue sky. Wherever one looked, it hung above the treetops, all slanting in the same direction. The carpet of the forest had holes in it now with a vengeance, and yellow patches of field gleamed peacefully among the dark green.

To build their houses these new arrivals used the material of which there was most available. For the walls they sometimes used ash and elm trees, or timber from the trees they felled to clear the ground. Osiers for wattle grew as thick as a week-old stubble along the fringes of the bogs, and farther in were beds of reeds that rustled in the wind. These were excellent for thatching. Sometimes, perhaps, if there were large stretches of grass available, they used sods to make the walls, or barked tree trunks, if the forest was thick and the trees stout where they were. But most frequently they used daub. There was always clay in the flat ground on which they had decided their houses should stand, and with their wooden spades they dug large, wide clay pits, for it takes a lot of clay to make a daub wall.

I became most painfully aware of that fact, because I wasn't able to site my houses near any of our materials, neither on clay soil nor close to a bog with osiers, or a wood with suitable trees. So all spring we fetched our materials from here and there. People round about were very kind and interested in our plan. Indeed, without their understanding of the importance of our being able to obtain just the materials we wanted, the whole thing would have been a fiasco.

I reckoned that we should need a thousand osiers, five hundred bundles of reeds or rushes, and ten tons of clay. No, ten tons would certainly not be too much. We fetched it one frosty day in March from an old frozen clay pit. It was the first time there was a lot of us, and we chopped and hacked our way through the frozen ground to the sticky clay beneath, and dug and dug until the weak, misted sun was low in the west. To transport this precious clay we borrowed a horse and a cart with rubber-tired wheels (our one concession to modernity). By the time we had unloaded the last of the clay, we were dead tired and dropping on our feet.

5. The Daub House

SINCE WE don't know what our forefathers called the various parts of their houses, we shall have to give them our own names.

Take you own house, for example. We are always using names like floor and ceiling and everyone knows what they are. But what is a ground sill? It is an old term for the foundations, which one makes first of all before one begins to build the walls.

What are the rafters? Go up into your attic and look at the roof. Or, if you can't do that, go to some place where they are building a house and the framework is finished. You will see a number of big triangles sticking up into the air, each formed of two big planks that meet in a point which forms the apex of a triangle. The sides of these triangles are the rafters, and each pair of rafters forms a truss, and the trusses, which are as close together as the ribs of a ship, together form the frame of the roof. If you stop to think, you will realize that it all would quietly collapse unless the trusses were supported. This is done with laths, which are long, narrow strips of wood nailed horizontally across the rafters, providing at the same time the support that the trusses need and something on to which to fix the tiles or other roof covering.

When the laths are nailed in place the whole thing looks rather complicated and, to make it even worse, each truss is strengthened internally. This is done, for example, by nailing or bolting a heavy crossbeam to the two rafters, thus forming a smaller triangle up under the roof. Should the two rafters now want to slip off the walls on which they rest, they won't be able to, because the crossbeam (called a tie beam) is holding them firmly together. In the old days, when there were no ceilings in houses, you could look straight up into the big, dark space of the roof, and it was on one of these crossbeams up there that the cock always perched. For that reason in some countries the tie beam is called a cock beam.

If you look at Plate IV it will make all this clear, if it isn't so already. But perhaps what you want to ask is why I have gone into all these

IV. This is how the rafters and transverse tie beams looked just before the attempt to erect them failed.

details of housebuilding when we are dealing with prehistoric houses and not present-day ones. The answer is that the difference between a modern house and a low, sway-backed, prehistoric hut is not nearly so great as you might think.

Even in prehistoric days the basic structure of a house was very similar to that of an ordinary modern house. Those prehistoric builders had exactly the same problems to overcome, and since they discovered what proved to be the best ways of solving them there has been no reason to change the principles they adopted or even to alter their methods. That is why, when I start describing how we tried our hands at the noble art of building a house (model 2000 B.C.), you will notice

30

that I use exactly the same terms as the builder does today, and by them mean the same things as he.

Here, now, is the task you are set:

You are to build a house for yourself and your friends, and it must be strong enough to withstand a normal winter's gale. It must be sufficiently weatherproof for you to be able to be reasonably dry in it, and not have draughts swirling around you in summer and a blizzard blowing in winter. In fact it is to be stout enough to stand for many years, and even after all the timbers in the ground have rotted away. And it must be practical, a house you can use.

And now comes the worst.

You are given definite instructions how the posts and the walls and the hearth have to be arranged.

That is the first half of the task. This is the second:

You are not to use spruce (which would be easiest to work on) and you must yourself fell all the trees you use. You mustn't use nails or wire. (Fancy not being allowed to have even a nail!) You mustn't use a saw, chisel, or hammer, but only an ax, and, to be quite correct, a stone ax.

There you are! Set about it.

The first thing you do, if you are me, is to scratch your head and stare at a great pile of material that you are supposed to turn into a nice cozy house of definite shape and appearance. Then you turn on your heel and hurry home and get out paper and pencil and write:

> DEAR JOHN: I'm going to build a house. Could you manage to come here for a weekend and give me a hand with it? We'll have a campfire every evening, lots of chat, and a grand time. If you come, bring your accordion with you, for even if it is a Stone Age house we're building, we're not going to twang catgut and bang on hollow tree trunks for our music.

After that you write thirteen other letters, and a few days later there is a shower of replies on postcards and letters, informing you in all sorts of scribbles and with all sorts of spelling mistakes, that they will all come and have already begun to file their teeth and hunt our mother's old lambskin coat or sheepskin rug, so that they can be like proper tough, hairy, savage Stone Age people.

Fourteen of them! you think. What about food? One person will eat five slices of bread and drink three glasses of milk for breakfast. Fourteen will eat seventy slices of bread and drink forty-two glasses of milk—for one breakfast! In eleven days (the rest of our holidays) fourteen people will eat seven hundred and seventy slices of bread and butter and drink four hundred and sixty-two glasses of milk (which makes about twenty gallons) for breakfast alone! To say nothing of all their other meals!

I went pale at the mere thought of it all. Yet without food and drink not even a hero can do much.

Then I went to my mother and told her that she would have to prepare herself to buy an oatmeal factory and a dairy and a bakery and a couple of fields of potatoes and a barrel of jam and a bullock or two. But Mother just smiled and said, "Well, Mr. Builder, you seem to have let yourself in for it. But never mind, your old mother wasn't born yesterday. She saw this coming and has stuffed her storeroom with jam, oatmeal, and a few other things."

I imagine that Mother must have counted the replies as they came in, but if you are going to build a house I advise you to have a talk with your mother first!

Down at the site the material lay all ready, just waiting for the glorious morning when the gang would be complete and we could make a start on our house. But I could not wait. Every evening I had to go down there and set up posts and poles, making queer scaffolding and towers, and scratch my head and consult my plans and measure with my rule and step out so many paces to the right and left, to and fro, in and out, till I had no real idea of what I was doing and began to feel discouraged and dread the day when the others would appear.

Then one day I heard a ghastly commotion on the road up to our house; it was a motor bike coming coughing up from the main road. Suddenly it stopped. This was the first of them—John. He had grown as much of a beard as he could muster, had a wrench in his teeth and an accordion on his back.

"Oh! thank God," he groaned. "For the last eight miles the clutch has only worked downhill, the brakes uphill, the front light when I drove into the ditch, and the carburetor when I sang—so I shall be more than glad to live a healthy primitive life for a bit, and meanwhile I'll stow the thing in your garage."

John laughed, and as if by magic all my despondency and hesitation vanished. Together we walked down to the site and I said, "There's no need to wait for the others, we might as well make a start today."

John nodded and scratched the back of his head as he gazed skeptically at the welter of tree trunks, heaps of clay, oisers, and bundles of reeds.

"Is this all going to be a—house?" he said.

"Here, take this spade and we'll dig the holes for the wall posts," I replied, handing John a spade and taking one myself. Shaking his head, he began to dig where I told him to.

"Here, you," said John. "You're using a steel spade. Did they have those in the Stone Age?"

"All right, all right," I said, "I've tried a wooden spade—there's one there! And those holes there were dug with it. But if we're going to get this job done in eleven days, we'll just have to use steel spades. But just you go ahead and try with a wooden one. You'll soon see what I mean."

John walked across and picked up the wooden spade. For a while he groaned and panted over it, then he flung it angrily away.

"That's not worth much," he said.

"It's worth a lot when you've got nothing else, and particularly when you use it properly. But of course you can't dig such a deep or narrow hole as you can with a steel spade. That's why, in the old days, they often preferred to dig a long trench for the posts, instead of a lot of difficult holes close together. Afterwards they filled up the intervening spaces with earth or stones and trod them down well, and the effect was the same."

After that it didn't take us long to dig all the holes for the wall posts. We dug them in a semicircle with about two feet between each, which was the distance that, after building my two trial houses, I had found to be the best if you wanted to be able to make a wattle wall of the right tension, not too loose or clumsy. There were sixteen post holes eighteen inches deep. By the time it was too dark to see any more John and I had not only dug all the holes for the wall posts, but we had barked some of the posts themselves. As the semicircular back wall was only to be some three feet high, the wall posts did not need to be more than four feet from the pointed end to the forked top that each of them had to have, but to carry the weight of the roof they needed to be five or six inches thick.

All the posts were of elm. John and I barked the trunks of young elms, peeling it off as though they had been bananas, for as long as bark is still fresh and sappy it comes off easily. To do this make a circular cut around the branch near the top, where the bark is becoming too thin to be serviceable, then make a deep cut all down the length of the branch (or stem) and carefully ease the bark off (see Fig. 9, F and G).

33

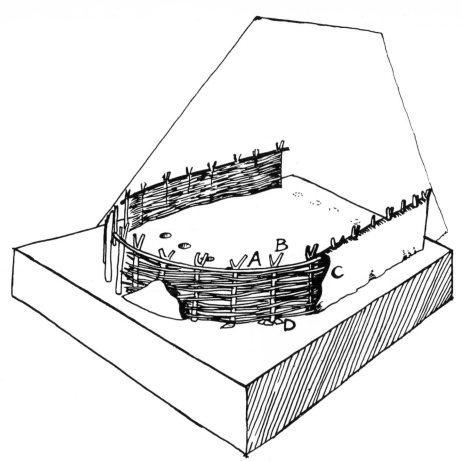

4. A, The wattle wall. On top the heavy "railing" or rim of the wall.   B, A post forked at its upper end.   C, A piece of ready daubed wall.   D, The tops of the stones holding the posts in place.

"Why are we barking the posts?" John asked, sucking his thumb that he had just cut. "Is it to make them look nice, or are you intending to feed us on bark?"

"No," I said, reaching for another suitable length of elm, "neither the one nor the other. You must remember all the bark we are going to need when the time comes to lash the laths to the rafters. We're not allowed to use nails or wire, and hemp rope or leather for thongs is too expensive to use in quantity. But elm bark is good and strong as long as you make sure it doesn't dry before you want to use it. So let me warn you that all that we're peeling off now has to be cut into strips, freed of its layer of cork, made into bundles, and laid in water this very night."

John surveyed his thumb sorrowfully, for some tannin had got into it.

V. The wattle has to be close and strong like the side of a gigantic basket.

VI. All the men and our one girl, my sister, treading the clay. When the picture was taken we still thought this amusing.

"It feels," he groaned, "as though a whole bottle of iodine had been poured into it."

John and I kept at it and did not leave off until the bark was cut into strips and we had a whole tubful of neat rolls of it. But by that time our eyes were smarting from lack of sleep and from the smoke of the campfire we had to make.

The next morning brought a series of shocks. The first and worst was that of having to get up at six, stiff in every limb, your throat feeling like a sandblasted drainpipe, face begrimed, and eyelids stuck together. Then there was the realization that I had invited fourteen young lads to come, and what on earth was I going to do with them all? Then,

VII. Bit by bit the wattle is daubed with clay.

after they had all arrived, there was the shock of discovering how much fourteen people can eat even before they have done any work at all.

The day saw as good as four thumbs cut off, one foot asking for immediate amputation, two cases of overexertion, innumerable scratches and cuts and minor wounds, blood on all our tools. And the final shock came when we found that there were not enough osiers to complete the house!

Despite these early difficulties we got the rest of the yellow, barked wall posts dug in in a semicircle, and wove a close fence of osiers between them. You do it like making a basket, only remember to alternate thicker branches with the thin, supple ones, or else the wattle won't be strong enough. (*See* Fig. 4 and Plate V.) If you ever go to the Friland's museum in Denmark, have a look at the old fences of woven osiers. That is exactly how the wall of a wattle-and-daub house looks before the clay is daubed onto the wattle. So you see that when the ancients built a house of material other than stone, whether in the Stone Age, Bronze Age, or Iron Age, they did it in just the same way as my companions and I did. The walls I think were probably the most correct thing about our house. That is the way they used to be made, and they could have been made in no other way.

There must too have been the same squelchy messy business of people jumping about in the clay in order to knead in with their feet (Plate VI), and the same groans and gasps from those who, with bowed backs, carried the wet clay in old skins to the wattle, on which it was then daubed to produce the complete wall. The only difference between us and the people of the Stone Age was probably the fact that my fourteen companions and I were doing the work for the first time, while our forefathers were probably made to help as soon as they could walk.

Some of us had tried it before, it is true. These were the ones who had helped me build my first wattle-and-daub houses, the little trial house about which I have already told you, and the other, larger one which we called the long house. My young sister was one of those early helpers. In the old days it was probably the women who did most of the kneading of the clay and who daubed it into the wattle, for the men would have had enough to do cutting the timber and fitting the rafters and ridgepoles for erection. We had only the one woman, my young sister, but she leaped about the clay heaps like a whole chorus of long-haired Stone Age maidens. Unfortunately there was quite a lot of flint in the clay, and in the end my sister cut her foot on a large, sharp piece and had to be sent up to Mother. It wasn't long, however, before she

38

VIII. The uneven surface is smoothed over with the palm of the hand.

IX. The great heap of clay has vanished, and instead we have a good, stout, daub-and-wattle wall. It dried quickly in the strong sun, but cracks have not yet begun to appear in it.

came limping back again with a pair of old galoshes tied to her feet, and at once she hopped up into the clay and again began paddling about in it up to her knees.

"Tough lass," Oliphant remarked, gouging clay out of one ear. "Sweet lass," said John, squinting down at a large bandage around one of his toes.

We worked steadily, and inch by inch the wattle was covered with a solid layer of clay. We had mixed hay with the clay in order to give it more cohesion and enable it to dry in larger pieces. When a section of the wall had been daubed with clay, first on the inside, then on the outside, the surface was smoothed over. We did this with the palms of our hands, which we kept wet by continually dipping them in water.

40

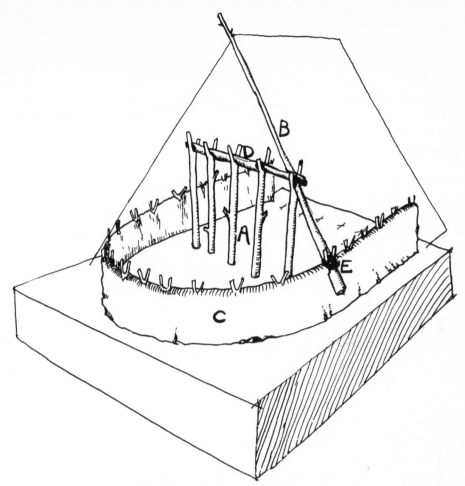

5. A, Supporting posts or pillars carrying the tie beam. Snags were left for later use as hooks.   B, The first rafter. Look too at Fig. 9, A and B, and you will see how they were fixed.   C, The finished wattle-and-daub wall.   D, The tie beam. Note how carefully it has been shaped to fit the forks before it was put in position.   E, The rafter is securely lashed with stout strips of bark.

In this way, we achieved a surface that was relatively flat and without bumps or bulges, so that rain and everything else striking the wall would be more likely to bounce off it again (Plates VII and VIII).

Then it began to rain, thoroughly and persistently. It was bad enough feeling a thick clay porridge running down our chests and back and into our trousers, but still worse to see the clay on the wall beginning to dissolve and losing its grip of the osiers and flopping to the ground with resounding smacks.

Fortunately I had seen this happen before and knew that we must pack the whole length of made wall with a thick layer of hay. Thus we surmounted the first of our many obstacles and completed the first stage of the house, but not our labors for the day. We still had to prepare for the next stage, and this meant cutting bark into strips and rolling it into neat coils, and this we did for what seemed like hours.

When we finally called it a day, one tired warrior remarked, "And in three hours we'll be up again, gay as larks, and go out into the nice green dry warmth of Mother Nature to enjoy the song of the dickey-birds and start work again and keep on at it for the next twenty hours, because of course we all feel that we get far too much sleep here."

That night we were indeed all gray with fatigue. We crawled into our piles of dusty, tickly hay, which seemed to harbor an infinity of insects, and collapsed. The stars peered down at us through the smoke hole, veiled every now and again by a puff from the smoldering embers. Inside reigned peace and quiet such as I had never experienced before, and when I closed one eye and listened, it seemed that the sounds of quiet breathing did not come from boys of the Atom Age, but from those who slept in a remote and distant past.

On the following day I can remember hearing nothing but the sound of axes, the heavy bump of the stone ax, and the angry chop of the steel ax (a further concession to our need to hurry), the rumble of rafters collasping, and the sighs of resignation from despairing housebuilders.

Our real difficulty, and the thing that was holding us back, was simply this: the great heavy rafters had to lean on the upper edge of the daub-and-wattle wall without breaking it, and without being able to slide down or be lifted or pulled up. At the same time the famous tie beam higher up had to have a good grip on the two rafters, so that they were never able to acquire too great a straddle.

That sounds all quite easy, but how was one to get the first truss to balance and not topple either forward or backward? The answer was: dig holes for several stout forked branches under the tie beam and let the tie beam rest on them (*see* Fig. 5). It was permissible to make holes, as there were post holes on the archaeologist's plan there, so that was all right; the only difficulty was that the rafters would not stay in place. The bark ties broke as if they had been cotton thread, and the whole truss kept collapsing inside the walls with a great rumble and crash.

Then we took our axes and cut flanges and notches, studs and holes, forks and supporting surfaces. Chips were flying all over the place, and what surprises me now is that no one chopped his—or anyone else's—foot off.

In the end the first truss sat in place. After that, having the recipe for the proper way of doing it, the rafters both for the semicircle and for the two side walls went up in no time at all. Soon most of us were sitting

42

X. Not an escaped monkey but one of the gang making the last bark tie to complete the skeleton of the house. The big beam in the foreground is the tie beam.

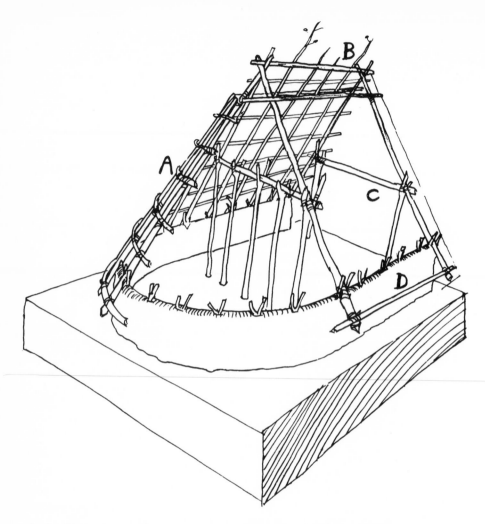

6. A, The rafters resting on the back wall are all brought together up above, where they meet on a cornice. For details see Fig. 9, C. On top of the rafters the laths are in the process of being lashed on.   B, The ridge of the roof connects the rear and front trusses, and on it all the rafters rest in pairs.   C, The tie beam in the gable.   D, The lowest lath on the long side of the roof.

up aloft at work on the structure of the roof, or perhaps just enjoying the view, but at all events looking quite small to those left on the ground and seeing us against the blue of the sky.

It was incredible how many lashings had to be made before all the rafters and laths were well and truly in place, and we had need of all the hands we had perched aloft, "welding" the framework of the house together and making it stout and pliant (*see* Fig. 6 and Plate X). By the time the shadows were lengthening and fatigue beginning to over-

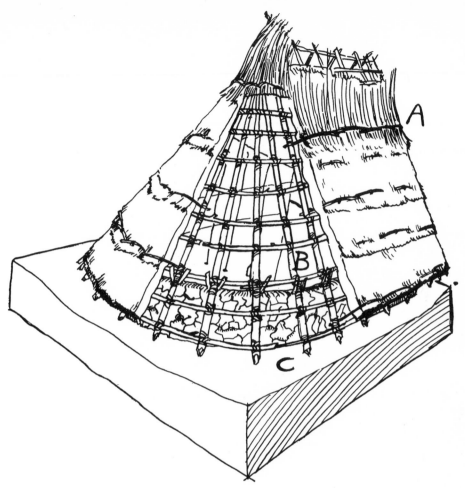

7. A, The last but one line of reeds has just been laid in place and secured. You can see the sticks which keep the thatch in place. Note the tie rod securing the reeds firmly to the roof. B, The corner of the frame carrying the thatch. Rafters and laths have to be lashed together in quite a considerable number of places. Note how, at the forks in the wall posts, every opportunity for extra strengthening of the rafters and laths is exploited. C, The wall is now quite dry and cracks are beginning to appear in the surface, but they don't matter.

come us, we had run out of bark, but also there were no more ties to be made, at least not that day.

The weather now turned dull and unpleasant, and at the same time we received a further four tons of clay, and lots more osiers. It was time to begin roofing the house.

Have you ever seen a thatch roof? I expect you have. You can thatch either with straw, which they never used in the old days because the straw of the grain they grew was not long enough, or with rushes from

XI. The roof has to be finished before the gable end can be closed. A roof looks vast when you begin work on it and the sun is blazing down and the rushes keep slipping through your fingers.

the bogs. Those who lived near the coast sometimes used seaweed and sometimes, I imagine, they just flung on a good thick layer of hay. But where they lived near a lake or a bog with great beds of rushes, the obvious thing was to use those.

You can use either fresh green rushes or rushes that have been cut during the winter. On fresh rushes the leaves are much larger and you lay the rushes with the root end uppermost and the leaves hanging downward. You start with a layer low down over your daub-and-wattle wall. The next layer you place so that it comes well down over the first,

8. The gable.

A, Wattle in the gable.   B, Hay. You can see how this is woven in Fig. 9, E. This covers and protects the vulnerable upper part of the wall.   C, The door. The curved piece of wood forms the top of the doorway. Here a cow's hide is being used to cover the opening, but it ought to be a wicker door made like the wattle in the wall.   D, The top of the roof needs a ridge to cover up the ends of all the reeds in the thatch. To keep this from being blown off in storms, heavy beams have to be hung across it.   E, The louver, covered by a leather flap.   F, The paving leading through the doorway.
G, The hearth.

and so you continue. Do that and not a drop of rain will get through (*see* Fig. 7 and Plate XI).

Our roof ended up a thing of bumps and bulges, and any decent thatcher would have fainted at the mere sight of it, but I wouldn't be surprised if it was pretty similar to the roofs of about three thousand years ago that we were trying to copy.

Each layer of rushes has to be tied to the lath under it so as to keep it in place and prevent it blowing away in a high wind. You do this with slender hazel rods laid across the rushes. A helper, sitting on a bar under the roof, pushes the end of a bark thong through the roof above the lath, the man on the roof takes this and pushes it back through the roof, but below the lath and over the hazel rod. The person inside then pulls the bark tight and, while the man on the roof puts his knee against the tie, knots it half a dozen times. And there you have the rod and the rushes firmly, immovably fixed.

47

XII. When a new house has to be inaugurated, you must dress up and feast all night.

It took a little time to acquire the right technique, but once we had, the work of roofing the house went quickly.

At this stage, by which time we had also started closing up the front gable with vertical wall posts including the two doorposts and the curved headsill for the doorway, which has to be a stout affair, the whole thing was really beginning to look like a house. I had found a tree with just the right curve for the headsill, which is wedged between the two doorposts. The space between the headsill and the tie beam was to be filled with close wattle and daubed with clay like the walls. The upper triangle, from the tie beam to the apex, was closed with compact woven hay. This space, of course, could have been filled with wattle-and-daub as well, but the ancients did not do that. The peak of the gable is very sensitive to movements of the house in storm and high winds, and also

48

XIII. A colorful gathering. It isn't the genuine Stone Age, but it gives an impression of the interior of one of their houses with the inhabitants gathered around the hearth.

it is hard work throwing clay up higher than you can reach, to say nothing of it being easier to pluck grass than to dig clay. What you do is to lash a number of sticks between the doorposts horizontally one above the other with a handsbreadth between each, and then taking twists of hay thrust them in and out through the spaces. The whole soon becomes a compact mass of hay. (*See* Fig. 8.)

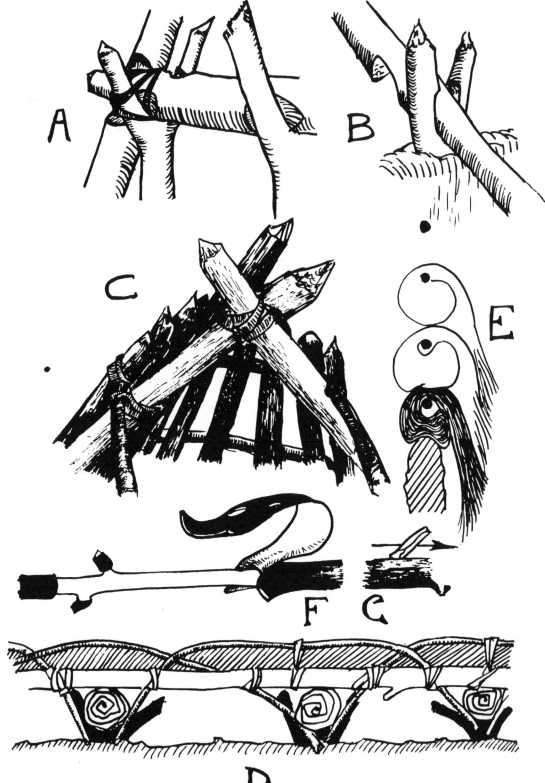

A

B

C

E

F   G

D

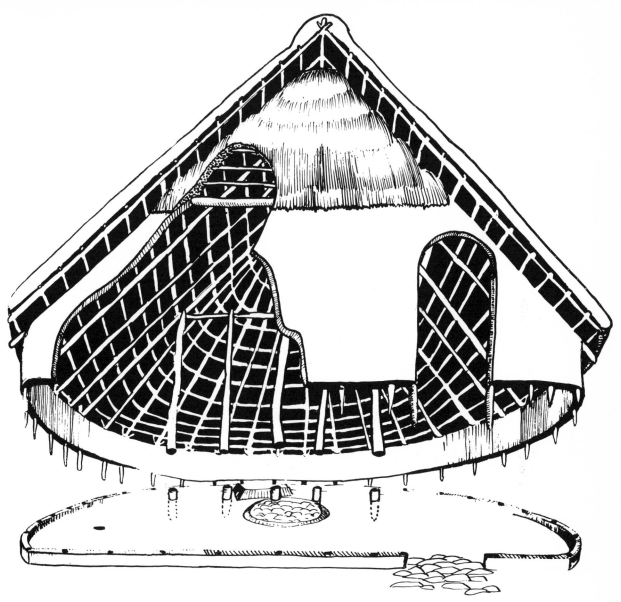

10. Here is the house opened up like a sardine tin so that you can see the details. In the middle is the hearth, the smoke from which filters out through the topmost triangle in the gable.

9. Detail (*left*).

A, Close-up of the join of the outer post, the rafter, and the tie beam. Where two trunks meet, or lie against each other, notches have to be cut or surfaces flattened so that they do not put too great a strain on the back ties.   B, The join at the wall. The rafter is not quite in place. You have to be careful not to make the notch too deep. C, The upper cornice where all the rafters of the semicircular wall meet. Notches are cut in the rafters so that they stay in place.   D, A vertical section of the roof just above the wall. Lowest is the wall itself, then the forked tops of the wall posts, the rafters resting in the forks. On top of these is a lath and on that the reed thatch. You can also see how the sticks are passed through the roof and lashed to the laths.   E, The technique used in weaving hay into the gable. This can also be used for a small roof or the actual walls.   F, Method of barking an elm trunk.   G, The bark can equally well be cut with a flint slice in the direction of the arrow.

We seemed too to be getting on faster, now that everyone could see that it really was going to be a proper house and not collapse in on us the day after we had put it up.

And so the house came to life. It had a nice shape. It looked well. We hurried on weaving the lower half of the gable into a close wattle of osiers, and filling the upper triangle with its twists of hay.

No sooner were we finished with the roof than the first of us was up on the fresh lot of clay, had spread a little hay on it, poured water over the hay and begun to trample in it, round and round, getting it ready for the gable. Soon a large amount of clay was spreading higher and higher up his legs, lumps of it were on his stomach and back, grinning at us from his face, and peering out from his hair. Whatever did other people think of us poor wretches who had to wallow in mud and mire from morning until night, all for the sake of a paltry house?

Haven't we all suffered from being told: "Be careful, don't get your nice clothes dirty. Don't make your hands filthy!" Oh to be able to leap into the world's largest mud puddle and get so dirty that one can never be clean or white again! Thank goodness, we were none of us fussy, otherwise the house would never have been finished.

Of course there were lots of things still to be done, important things like the wattle door for the door opening, the hearth, and the louver through which the smoke was drawn out. In this the door plays a big part. As long as it is shut, so that there is only a narrow gap between it and the ground, the smoke will rise and make its way out, gradually filling all the upper part of the roof space, but no more, unless it is a day with heavy pouring rain. But if the door is wide open the smoke swirls about and it is far from pleasant inside. The louver itself consists of the topmost peak of the gable, which is given a little frame and left free of hay. Through this the smoke filters out and a little daylight in. Then there was the clay seat, the paving of stones in the doorway and in front of the house, and all the little holes and gaps that remained to be stopped up. But even so you could say that on the whole the house was finished, and that evening I was able to announce: "We are going to light the first fire in the new house and inaugurate it. Mother is to come down, because she has had a large share in our being able to build it."

We celebrated the building of our new house with song and accordion music until far into the night. Our work was over and no longer should we hear the sound of Mother's big Norwegian cowbell telling us that a meal was ready, or the answering blare of our oxhorn announcing that the Stone Agers were ready and coming.

52

6. The Law of Fire

Do YOU know the law of fire?

You shall learn it now. From the day the first man fetched fire from a burning tree or from the flame-spewing mouth of the great volcano (as it was then) Akka, he and his descendants for thousands of generations have been subject to the law of fire.

The ancients had gods who were great; the Sun God and the God of the Ax and the God of Fertility; but it was the God of Fire who was closest to them. When for a time the Sun God just grew weaker and weaker, so that the nights lengthened and became blacker and blacker, all that was evil and dangerous emerged and flourished. Wolves and other ravening beasts prowled about on the outskirts of the forest, sometimes making sorties across the fields right down to man's dwellings. And when snow was swirling or the frost bright and sparkling, other invisible beings emerged, many of them the souls of the dead who had not been buried along with their kin, and the souls of animals that had been killed. In the black depths of the great bogholes, or in the quietly gliding water of the sreams, lived beings who had to have gifts made for them before one could pass that spot. Big mossy boulders were dangerous if they did not receive a gift, and stones on which a human being had been sacrificed were especially savage and cruel.

A horde of unknown powers surrounded man's dwellings in a ring, or lurked at the edge of the forest. When the nights grew long it seemed to the inmates that this ring contracted, and finally came close up to their dwellings, icy and menacing.

They made sacrifices then and gave gifts to all the friendly powers, set meat and mead in front of the symbol of the God of the Ax, a great strong ax that was set up in the ground in a special corner of the house. By day they took earthenware vessels with food up to their dead kinsmen, in order to induce them to make the day longer and beseech the Sun God to return. To protect themselves against the strange beings that visited the village at night, they laid amulets in front of their doors and drew sacred symbols in the snow and mud outside.

53

XIV. Cracked and dented, the daub walls go on drying. From now on it will be left to wind and weather to smooth them down.

Fire was the gift of the gods. Little pieces of it shone in the skies at night, and the Sun God even had one wheel of his chariot made of fire.

Fire was mightiest when the gods wrestled high up over the forest, and great crashes pealed out and rolled on across the country. The aerial contest of the gods was sacred and good, for shortly afterwards life-giving rain came pouring down over the dry, dusty fields. People went out and stood in the rain and watched the tremendous unruly fires flashing in the stream of raindrops pouring down onto the thatch roofs and splashing onto the village street. Muddy torrents swept past them, carrying off husks and gnawed bones.

It could happen then that fire would come darting out of the sky and crash into the fringe of the forest across the fields. There would be a

XV. Primitive houses are rather like live beings. You feel that at any moment a Stone Age man will step out through the doorway.

sulphurous smell in the air and where the fire had struck, the trees and bushes would be aflame, while inside the houses of man the flames of the fire on his hearth bowed down respectfully and the smoke refused to go out through the louver. Then the people no doubt fell on their faces and worshiped the mighty god who could do anything so tremendous.

Fire was alive. It muttered and chattered on its hearth. The fireplace was its dwelling and to trample in it was sacrilege. It was the heart of the house, and around it those who dwelled in the house gathered in wintertime. In fact our forefathers spent much of their lives around the leaping flames, so no wonder they were attached to their fire and cared for it.

Stories were told as they sat around the fire on the hearth. While the

XVI. Not an African Negro's hut, but our semicircular house seen from the rear.

teller told his tale the others filed fishhooks or knives from heavy, smooth bones, or hardened hafts for their skin scrapers and other tools in the fire, and the women spun fishing lines and wove baskets, sewed bark into boxes, or ornamented delicate little pots.

There was enough to do, for in those days you could buy nothing except a woodman's ax which you got from the flintsmith, or ceremonial vessels from the potter.

When a storm blustered over the house and set it swaying and rocking beneath the pressure of the wind, the people edged closer together and tried to forget the evil outside.

The grandfather, with his bony, old man's body and brown skin tanned by wind and weather, sat cutting thin strips of leather with a sharp piece of flint. Those thongs would be used as lashings for spear-heads and hunting axes, arrows, and animal traps. Some perhaps would be used to sew the seams of the big skin boats they had been planning for years to build, but of which nothing had yet come. And as he filed away at the skins he told legends and exciting tales of hunting.

One of the favorite tales of the children was that of how the forests and the animals, the sky and the birds, the sea and its fish, came into being. It was a long and good tale. It set their imaginations working.

Sometimes the old grandfather told them stories of the times when the tribe came marching in to take possession of these new lands. In those days people were very different, not so spineless as they are now, he would add, glaring at the boys around the fire; but they only laughed.

This treasure store of exciting tales and legends has been lost forever, so immense is the distance in time between the Stone Age and now. But just as of all their names for gods and people, animals and spirits and places, only a few can be traced here and there, so perhaps a little of their legends still exist, but inextricably entangled in the additions of the centuries that have since come and gone.

It is a great pity that we don't know what tales and stories they told, but four thousand years is a tremendous obstruction, and it is only cold dead things, their tools, household utensils, and grave goods, that can speak to us now.

My companions and I had to learn the laws of fire too. We did not tend our fire as we should, we were irreverent and did not see that there was always someone in attendance. So one day the fire rose, stretched up, and reached for the roof. Straw and rush heads began to glow and curl up in the ties. Then it got hold of the roof. Suddenly we saw its face appear over the ridge of the roof, and our hearts went into our mouths in horror.

We did what we could to master the fire, labored by the sweat of our brows. We fought for the house that we had toiled so hard to build and in which we had spent so many happy hours. But the fire grew and grew, became a giant. Hissing, is spread along the underside of the roof, then rose up like an ogre and took the roof up with it into the air.

What could one do then but give up—and feel small, for such powers are beyond one. The flames twisted and turned on high, some even went riding up on great soaring tufts of the roof. There was a great crackling and roaring as the God of Fire vented his wrath on our house. The heat became so fierce that we had to withdraw quite a distance to watch our handiwork being destroyed and collapsing, rafter by rafter—it was as

XVII. Woe unto you, when the flames are rising over your house, for then it is in the
power of the God of Fire, and he is implacable.

though something of ourselves had burned as well, leaving an emptiness
inside us.

At last the Fire God himself fell silent and sank down below the now
blackened daub walls. Then there was silence everywhere, except for the
loud, clear song of the grasshoppers in the bushes. We felt as if the fire
had embraced the whole world, although it was only a thing of our own
that had burned. Carefully and respectfully we stepped onto the fire
ravaged floor, still hot and now open to the sky, to see if anything had
survived. Yes, there was the oxhorn; but it had fallen silent forever, for
when we touched it, it turned into black powder.

The memory of that day is firmly imprinted on our minds, and our advice to you is: profit by our bitter experience and remember to respect the law of fire.

All that remained was a black expanse between bare, hard-baked, daub walls. But even that had its use, for nothing was moved until everything had been measured, sketched, and photographed. The knowledge we thus gained will perhaps help interpret a real site of a house that had burned far back in the Stone Age.

7. The Flintsmith and the Gray Skin Boat

THAT SUMMER I paid a visit to a real flintsmith. His name was Anders Kragh and he lived on Gjol, a peninsula in Limfjorden. It was a great event for me, for I had my own experience of flint and knew only too well how difficult it is to make things out of it. I had tried and failed. How one made a big woodman's ax or a broad double-edged dagger or a long flint spearhead was still a mystery to me, as to most people, and I would have given much to see how a real flintsmith chipped such elegant things.

Like the bronze caster in the Bronze Age and the blacksmith in the Iron Age, the flintsmith of the Stone Age was an especially important person, and had a big say in the affairs of his village and surrounding district. From him alone you could buy the precious axheads that were so important when some more of the forest had to be cleared or a new house built. Those who were especially rich and powerful could get him to make them those big delicate daggers and spearheads that were the insignia of their greatness when journeying away from home.

The flintsmith did not associate with ordinary folk, for his was a difficult art and required the help of powers that were not available to just anyone. So he lived in a little house out on a small island or in a bog, at all events at some distance from the village. No one knew how he made his things, and he taught his art only to his own son or to a specially chosen apprentice.

Being the only man able to make things which were absolutely necessary for the life of the community, the flintsmith was able to charge well for his goods. An ax was expensive and you had to fork out many a beaver skin and measure of grain before you became owner of such a treasure. Ordinary chips and scrapers most people could manage to make themselves, but if an ax chipped and the owner tried to put a new edge on it the result was deplorable.

As time went on, life became less easy for the flintsmith. Itinerant traders began to appear who had shiny axes and spearheads of yellow

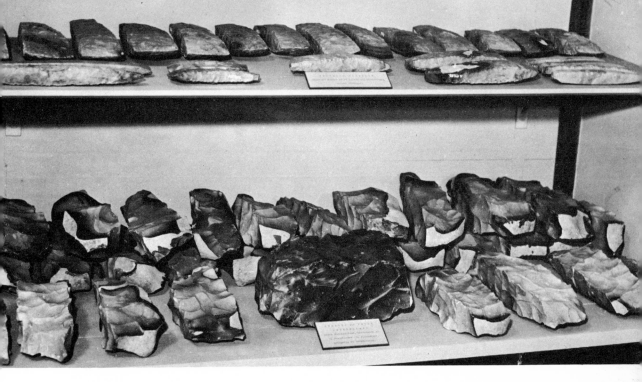

XVIII. A typical museum showcase with axes and flint bars in neatly ordered rows; but they are not really at home behind glass.

metal for sale. They only came at long intervals, it is true, but the mere fact that they came meant that what the flintsmith made now had to be superior to these newfangled tools and weapons, or the smith would be put out of business, as eventually happened everywhere. But for a long time the metal tools and weapons were so expensive that even the great had to think twice about buying them, and often shook their heads and pointed to their flint daggers when they met one of these merchants. But you couldn't make as many things in flint as in metal, and the days of the flintsmiths were numbered.

Not all flint is equally good. The old hunters of the early Stone Age probably had to make do with a chance block of flint found on the forest floor or on the beach, and this answered the purpose well enough, for clever though they were at chipping their small hunting axes and slender thin edges for their harpoons and arrows, they never tried to make anything really big.

The large, double-edged flint axes that the farmers of the New Stone Age used were the result of a new and difficult technique of chipping, and called for a very even, tough flint. Because of that the flintsmith had to get his flints from a flint mine. The art of mining had been learned

61

by then and such things existed. Where limestone and chalk shone whitely through the turf or from a cliff face, there the men sank a broad shaft, and when they reached a layer of flint they dug galleries out on all sides. We have found some of these mines, and even those of which we know must have employed considerable numbers of people. At the mouth of the shaft of the mine worked the men whose job was just to chip the dented, shapeless slabs of flint into quadrangular lumps, large bar-shaped ones for axes, smaller and more slender ones for daggers and spears.

On beaches where there was a wealth of flint these chippers must have sat, one beside the other, working away. We can still find traces of their activities, and in some places they have left so many flint bars that bulldozers have shoveled them up by the mouthful. It would seem these were stores to which a flintsmith could go and select his own material according to his needs, and take it back with him to his forest fastness.

In some districts of course there were neither flint mines nor flint deposits, and in these places people were willing to pay almost anything for a good flint ax to take the place of the small granite axes which were all they could make for themselves. Thus, while in the south of Europe people were cleverly mining copper ore and exporting it, the Stone Age people of Denmark and elsewhere were exporting flint in large quantities to Sweden, Norway, and many other places. Much of this trade went overseas, and if you think they used hollowed-out tree trunks for cargo boats you are wrong. The flint bars were stowed in the bottom of a big skin boat, and in such craft they were often carried across considerable stretches of sea. These were big boats, and large crews were needed to paddle them and their heavy loads to their destinations. Many no doubt were lost, but many successfully reached the lands of the many islets and deep, steep-sided fiords in the north, while others went southwards to the wide flat lands of the big estuaries where the tribes were numerous and rich.

Now and again a battered skin boat would put into a trading place. It had been almost as far as to where the Sun God drove his chariot into the sea, and from there it had brought red, smooth copper axes, or half-moon-shaped ornaments of soft yellow metal. These men had been so long under way, on the journey out and home, that they had seen open sea all summer.

This was the beginning of the great trade routes that the men of the north later made their own, once people had learned to sew planks to-

XIX. A stone ax feels at home in the bottom of a Greenlander's skin boat. The difference between this boat and the craft that were used to export flints across the seas is not great.

gether to make wooden ships capable of carrying many people. But that was already the Bronze Age.

When I visited my flintsmith, I saw him chipping off splinters and chips as accurately and neatly as you could wish. You could scarcely believe it possible. It had taken him twelve years of his free time to discover and acquire the difficult technique, for there was no one who could teach him. He had had to begin from the very beginning, as I had, but he had been at it for twelve years and I for scarcely four. But I got so much out of my visit that after a little while all I could remember was that my dream had come true.

Today the flintsmith doesn't require an apprentice in order to ensure that his skill and knowledge shall not be lost. He can write a book explaining it all, and the various problems, and then others can use that knowledge and perhaps learn to cut flints even more quickly or better.

Before he does so, let me tell you a bit about this modern flintsmith's methods. He doesn't just take a piece of flint and bang away at it. If you do that, bits will fly off, of course, but not in the right place. The first thing you must do is to make a "point of application." If, for example, you wish to split a flint in a certain direction, you must first mark out the surface you want to have left, and this you do by making a groove all the way around the flint. Anders Kragh selects a block of flint that is roughly rectangular, and of the size and shape of the thing he wishes to make. If he now wants to split this lengthwise, he will first make a small hollow in the end of the flint from which the split is to begin. He has discovered that to make this hollow he cannot just chip at the flint; he has to use an anvil. This is a pointed stone. He takes his piece of flint and rests it against the point of the anvil at the spot where he wants to have the hollow. Then he strikes the flint, so that it looks as though he were trying to split it from the wrong end, but the flake that does come off comes not from where he struck, but from where the flint rested against the anvil. He then puts the point of the anvil in the hollow he has made and deals the top of the flint a hard blow that must land on the exact spot, and off flies a great flake of flint, perhaps the length of two fingers, split from the point of impact down to the hollow. It is this technique that has enabled him to make such fine daggers and spearheads that the experts cannot tell them from the real Stone Age ones. He has thus proved that the husbandmen of those days could have made double-edged axes and been able to fell stout oaks and clear the forest from their villages and fields.

As I cycled away from the flintsmith's house I could see the calm, summery, smooth expanse of Limfjord shining on the horizon. The road was deserted but for two boys who seemed very busy. Each had a stone which he rested on the asphalt while he hammered on it with another heavy stone. They were so intent that they neither saw nor heard anything, scarcely the flying chips that flashed in the air around them.

I stopped.

"What are you making?" I asked, though I could see perfectly well what they were about.

"We're cutting flints. We are going to be flintsmiths."

"Are you indeed. Where did you get that idea?"

"There's a man here who makes beautiful things of flint and we want to learn to do the same."

They were too busy for talk, so I rode on down the sun-baked road. For a long time I could hear the sound of their hammering behind me, and it occurred to me that that sound was no stranger to the countryside. Indeed, it must have been a commonplace of life there for over ten thousand years.

Ling-cling-cling, it rang out behind me as I rode on; then, finally, the sounds died away.

8. I Turn Potter

THE WORK of the Stone Age flintsmith is hard enough, but it isn't much easier to make Stone Age clay pots and bake them in fires built in the open. I tried, and though on my desk there now stands a row of quite nice little pieces, I can claim to be nothing more than a mediocre potter, for the shards of my failures would certainly more than fill my whole room.

The thing began when we decided that we needed a certain modest vessel down by the house. That started us off, but we ended by going on and on until we had copied the hitherto largest clay vessel known from the New Stone Age, which was some twenty inches high and the same in diameter.

What are the clay vessels of antiquity like?

Your mother will have all sorts of pots, pans, cups, jars, and flower-pots, and these are all things she can buy in a shop when she needs one, but if you had been living in the Stone Age she would have had to make all her pots and pans and things herself.

The oldest tribes, who only hunted, did not know how to make vessels of clay, and had to manage with boxes made of birch bark and buckets made of leather. Such things are perfectly serviceable, but they have one great failing; you cannot put them over a fire. In those days, if they wanted to make soup or to boil anything, they had to drop red-hot stones into some bark container. The people of the kitchen middens did make a few clumsy coarse vessels with pointed bases for sticking down into the coals of a fire; but, apart from these, the first earthen vessels were copies of the leather bucket, birch-bark box, and vessels made of gourds —calabashes.

The tribes that had an unsettled existence roaming from area to area, as did the first crop-growing tribes before they reached the new lands and settled down, carried their earthenware vessels in carrying nets or wicker holders. When, after many centuries, they finally lost the urge to roam and settled down, they no longer needed carrying nets or wicker holders; yet, to their minds, an earthenware vessel was not right without a net, it was like a lamp without a shade to us, or a steamer without a funnel. A vessel had to have a net, and so the women and girls drew a net or wickerwork on the wet clay. Sometimes they even put on strips of clay to look like withes or thongs. That is the origin of the oldest patterns on earthen vessels, and people went on using the same patterns and seldom changed them deliberately.

It was many generations before new shapes were invented, but in the end the lines of the carrying nets that they used to draw on the sides of the vessels resolved into dashes and dots, and then they began making quite new patterns by pressing the edge of a mussel shell or a jagged piece of stick into the clay.

The ancient dwelling places show a very definite line of development up through the ages. The ancients did not suddenly start putting on a lip or a spout here and there, and making queer jars with abstract patterns on them. They were very painstaking, and anyway things usually went wrong if they ever ventured to draw on the clay. No, a girl made the same sort of vessels as her mother did and as her grandmother had before that, regarding these as the only serviceable ones. In the end, people had been copying the leather buckets and bark boxes so long that the origins were forgotten and they began to venture to curve the brim more and more either in or out, and to make the belly more and more pronounced. In time their shapes became so wild and clumsy that finally they were more ugly than beautiful, and it was many years before the simple and slender returned to favor. Thus you find style going in waves, and that makes it possible for us today to distinguish between the different epochs.

Some vessels were given faces, and so they became alive and were able to join in everything that went on. Others were made particularly delicately, with thin sides and an even, uniform firing and a close, delicate pattern inlaid with chalk. These were for ceremonial occasions and also, filled with food and drink, for the dead to have with them when they were laid in their barrows. Sometimes a number of vessels have been found outside, at the mouth of a megalithic tomb, and at the same site others with burial gifts inside have been found beside the skeletons of the dead. Those vessels outside must have contained gifts, put there for the ancestors in the hope that they would help when someone at home was ill; or else they were tokens of gratitude given when the harvest or hunting had been good. They were placed outside because those making the gifts didn't dare go any farther.

XX. First you make the base, the open saucer to the left of the two finished vessels, then a ring is shaped and . . .

In the Bronze Age the custom was to burn the dead. People no longer believed that the dead just lived on inside the burial mounds, but instead that by being burned they were dedicated to the great Sun God. They now made special earthen vessels called funerary urns to hold the ashes of the dead. Sometimes they made a little door in the urn, so that the dead person's soul could get out, if it happened to have been shut in accidentally.

One of my friends who lived nearby was going to be a potter, so when I decided to try to make my Stone Age vessels I enlisted his help. I thought that if he and I worked together we should get much further than if I did everything alone.

XXI. . . . placed on top of the base. But wait till you are attempting something really big. It isn't so easy then!

A vessel is made in three stages; first it has to be fashioned in wet clay, then it has to dry, then it has to be baked. The baking is the worst.

In the old days the potter's wheel was known and used away down in the Mediterranean area, but up in the north vessels were built up of strips of clay.

We began by making small earthen vessels, and pretty squat and thick-walled they were, just like the oldest ones in the museums. At this stage we didn't dare dream of making ones large enough to hold even a quart.

Gradually we learned from experience. We discovered that it was best to beat the strips of clay slightly flat at one edge so that they could be smoothed out into each other more easily, and that it was better not to

69

XXII. A whole family of vessels we made, but unfortunately these all exploded when we tried to fire them. It was not till later that we discovered the correct method.

put the strips on in a spiral pattern, but as rings one on top of the other. Anything over a certain size had to be made in several stages, and our experience was that it was best to make the bottom first and then build the vessel up, but always keeping the base uppermost. That made the walls slope in toward each other, so that the many pounds of wet clay used were supported in the same way as an arch. Before we tried that method, one vessel after another had just collapsed, but the new method allowed us to be far more venturesome and to build bigger and bigger vessels. Once some of the moisture in the clay had evaporated and the base become a little tougher, you could turn the vessel over, make the rim or neck, and feel reasonably certain that you wouldn't find the whole thing as flat as a pancake the next morning.

70

XXIII. First, you put the dry vessel in
the bottom of a shallow pit . . .

XXIV. . . . then you pile charcoal and
dry branches around and over it . . .

The drying process cost us a lot of vessels, especially the big ones of twenty or thirty pounds. It is infuriating to find something over which you have taken endless trouble spoiled by great vertical cracks in the sides caused by its drying too fast. But it is the firing that is the really critical thing.

Our first attempt at firing a vessel went rather like this: A lovely earthen vessel had been in the flaming fire for exactly ten seconds when there was a dull bang, the potter thrust his head into the flames thinking there might be a flint in the fire, but pulled it out again quickly and, looking up at me in surprise, said, "The thing's gone." Boom! it went again and a salvo of red-hot shards whistled past, just where his eyes had been.

71

XXV. . . . light your fire, and, when it is
burning well, cover it all over with sods.

XXVI. Next morning open up carefully
—and with thumping heart—and behold,
the miracle!

All our attempts ended in bangs like fireworks, as vessel after vessel disintegrated. Small drinking beakers and big storage jars all vanished. We decided that we must be using clay that was too greasy and so could not stand the sudden heat from the fire. Or that we had forgotten to mix sand with the clay, as you must.

Eventually we gave up the open fire and took to firing our vessels in a closed stack. That took longer, but the heat was not so violent and the results were much better. But the first time the stack was too exposed and the second time it was too deep, and on both occasions the pots cracked.

"We'll have plenty of shards for the floor," became our motto.

Late one evening we walked down to open three stacks that had been burning since noon. The one we opened first was the fifteenth we had made and in it was the thirtieth vessel that had come from our hands. We had lanterns, and by their light we could see through the smoke and steam that the usual thing had happened; cracked through in all directions. It was the same with the next stack; all cracked. But in the third the vessel was whole. Big and lovely it was and there wasn't a crack in it. After that our luck turned and we had more and more whole vessels.

The stacks in the photographs are small ones, but there is no reason why they should not be larger and capable of taking several vessels. You can stack peat or charcoal round the vessels as long as they have a "cloak" of hay or reeds to protect them at the beginning. If you want to be quite safe, put a bucket or your biggest earthen vessel upside down over them—that will protect them from too great and sudden heat.

11. Stone ax and earthen vessel. Here you see my ax with which I felled the first tree, and my first successful pot. You can imagine how fond I am of both.

73

9. Plowing and Sowing Summer Wheat

I SUPPOSE it is not all that long time ago that my companions and I used to make ourselves bows and arrows and spear shafts, and I can remember how difficult it was in town to get hold of anything like a decent branch of willow for our bows. Once we had moved out to the country, however, I found this mysterious and hitherto all but unknown tree everywhere.

Near my home we found what we called Horser Land, an overgrown old bed of marl with clifflike formations and deep little lakes, as wild and eerie as proper alps. We lived in Horser Land, which was our refuge from our mortal enemies, the Palefaces, who pursued and shouted at us from the edge of the marl. There we had plenty of material for our weapons, so much that we were able to pick and choose, as you always must in order to get exactly the right kind of branch you need. That gave us an idea of how much measuring and searching must be involved when you want to build a boat, to say nothing of a Viking long ship.

We needed trees that had grown in various ways for building our houses and for hafts and handles of various kinds. The ancients were accustomed to this, of course, and must have had a much better eye for the possible uses of a nice crooked branch than we had, for it certainly took us a lot of searching to get what we needed. My hardest search, however, came when I decided to try to build a proper prehistoric plow. This was made of wood and called, in Denmark, an *ard,* which is a much older word than plow and has gone into English as *arder,* the old, old term for plowed land. An ard cannot turn the earth like a modern plow, for it has no moldboard, which is a board wedged into one side of the plow that tips the earth over onto that side so that it is properly turned. An ard is just driven through the ground like a stick and throws as much earth to one side as to the other.

There are two kinds of ard. One is a hook ard, which is just a big

74

XXVII. The oldest agricultural instrument is the mattock, and the oldest mattocks were made of elkhorns; they work beautifully in the good mold we have today, but it must have been a different story in the Stone Age, when the ground was full of stones and tree stumps.

XXVIII. My mother once said that my ard was like a musical instrument. It was beautifully balanced.

mattock with a shaft that oxen pull along, and a handle bar. This is the oldest form of the ard and it was used in the days when people lived in the type of house I had built, and even much later. The other is called a bow ard, and this is just an ordinary wooden spade harnessed to a pair of oxen by means of a long curved pole, and it was this that I made, using just my ax. As you can see from the picture, it is quite a complicated instrument, and has a number of parts for which different kinds of wood were needed.

It is a queer experience making a complicated tool without knowing why the different parts have the shape they do. The ard I made was a copy of one found in a peat bog, where it had been laid out as a gift for

76

XXIX. They ought to have been oxen, but there were none. It took some time before we learned the art of keeping the plow in the ground.

the gods. By using pollen analysis, it was possible to date it to the latter part of the Bronze Age or earliest Iron Age. Thus my ard was a faithful copy, while my houses were reconstructions.

The day came when I had to try my tool out. It must have been comical to see us draw the first few furrows in tough, long stubble. The horses, which had to do duty as oxen, walked off at a good pace, and we zigzagged down the big field. At first I found it almost impossible to keep the plow in the ground, but as time went on I learned how to steer it, and not only that, but I also discovered why the various parts were shaped as they were.

It is a wonderful experience to walk up and down a field behind a plow, your hand on its steering bar, and find yourself suddenly transported out of your own time into that of your remote forefathers.

My forefathers had plowed that field. In those days the fringe of the forest had been just beyond the rise and the plow must have kept twisting

XXX. Wheat growing against the daub-and-wattle wall of our Stone Age house.

and sticking because of all the thousands of stones that raised their gray pates everywhere. They plowed the field this way and that, crisscross, and then sowed their wheat or barley in poorly weeded furrows. Since that day the sun has passed through the sky overhead more than a million times. So near and so inconceivably remote is the time when our Stone Age ancestors were alive.

My plow, I feel, has let me glimpse a little light in the darkness that prevails far down the ages, and I say to you:

Cherish the memory of the ancients and protect the few remaining traces of them.

Materials Needed for Our Stone Age House

CLAY for the walls, floor, and hearth	9 tons.
REEDS or RUSHES for the roof	220 bundles (or armfuls).
HAY for the gable, for mixing in the clay, for the roof ridges, etc.	Much more than you expect. We used a whole truck load.
OSIERS and HAZEL TWIGS for the wattle of the walls, tie rods for the thatch, and many other things	Best have 2,000 so as to have some in reserve.
POSTS for the low wall, 4 ft. 6 in. to 5 ft. 4 in., thick, forked	28.
POLES for supporting tie beams, 8 ft. by 5 in., forked	10.
POLES for rafters, 13 ft. and not less than 2 in. thick at the thinnest point	28.
LATHS and TIE RODS, not less than 1 in. in diameter	Difficult to estimate, you can best judge from your own plans.
POSTS for doorposts, topping the daub-and-wattle wall, and holding the roof ridge in place, 6 ft. by 4 in.	10.
BARK from your elm stems	
STONES for paving and the hearth (not flint in the hearth as that explodes when very hot)	
FOOD	Lots and lots.